THE STEP BY STEP ART OF
Christmas Crafts

CLB 4093
This 1994 edition published by
Tiger Books International PLC, London
© 1994 CLB Publishing, Godalming, Surrey
All rights reserved
Printed and bound in Italy
ISBN 1-85501-602-8

THE STEP BY STEP ART OF
Christmas Crafts

JAN EATON

TIGER BOOKS INTERNATIONAL
LONDON

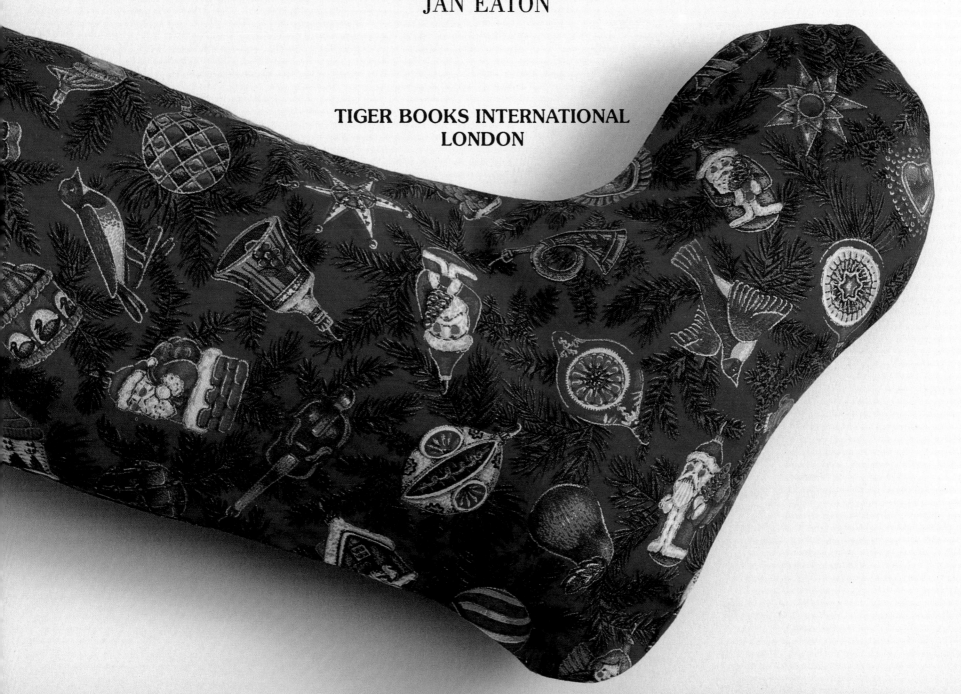

Contents

Techniques

The following pages demonstrate clearly and concisely the craft techniques involved in the festive projects presented in the book. They include dried flower arranging, papier mâché and other paper crafts, salt dough modelling, fabric and silk painting as well as embroidery. Before you start any project, carefully read through the instructions for the relevant technique outlined here and practise the methods required.

Ribbon bows
Double-looped bow: *Make 2 ribbon loops on either side of your thumb and forefinger leaving a similar length of hanging ribbon on either side as tails. Cut ribbon and twist one end of a 22 gauge stem wire (page 11) around the middle. Tie ribbon around the middle to cover the wire.* **Single-loop without tails:** *As above but make only one loop and do not make tails*

Swag base
Cut a strip of wire netting 20 cm (8 in) wide. Fill with sphagnum moss, packing tightly since the 'rope' needs to be quite solid. Wrap the netting around the moss and twist the cut wire ends around the netting to secure.

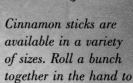

Wiring a terracotta pot

Place a small piece of dry foam into a pot so that it fits snugly. Thread an 18 gauge wire (see opposite) through the bottom of the pot and between the foam and the side of the pot. The pot can then be wired onto a swag base.

Wiring dried flowers, cinnamon, nuts and cones

When decorating with or arranging dried flowers, it is best to attach the flowers and other material, either singly or in bunches, to lengths of wire, since their own stems are often too thick or brittle. Wiring also helps to create a more solid arrangement. You will need 18 or 22 gauge stem wires, the 18 gauge being the strongest and used if the wire is to be the only support for the bunch.

Take a bunch of dried material and cut stems to the required length – usually 12.5-17.5 cm (5-7 in). Hold stems together tightly at the bottom between thumb and forefinger. Bend a wire about two thirds of the way along its length to form a loop. Place the loop under the bunch and hold in place with the third finger. Firmly twist the longer portion of the wire 5 or 6 times around the bunch, but not too tightly to break the stems. Single flowers, such as roses, are wired in the same way.

Cinnamon sticks are available in a variety of sizes. Roll a bunch together in the hand to make them fit together. Hold the bunch tightly, place a wire around the middle and twist the ends together several times. To wire a walnut, dip the end of a 22 gauge wire into latex-based adhesive, then push into the nut base where the two halves join. Leave to dry. Small and medium-sized cones are wired with 22 gauge wires; larger cones require 18 gauge wires. Loop a wire around the cone close to the base. Twist the ends together tightly. Trim the stems of artificial fruits leaving a short length. Wire in the same way as flower bunches or single flowers.

Binding stems

Tightly wind stem binding tape twice around the top of a wire stem or bunch to cover the wire. Hold firmly between thumb and forefinger and with the other hand pull the tape downwards so that it stretches. Turn the stem between thumb and forefinger while continuing to pull the tape downwards so that it twists around the length of wire.

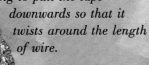

Papier mâché – layered method

1 *Many types of paper can be used to make papier mâché but newspaper is the most versatile. Tear the paper into strips along the grain of the paper. A large, flat surface can be covered with strips 5 cm (2 in) wide but areas with corners or curves may need strips as narrow as 3 mm ($^1/_8$ in). It may be necessary to tear the strips into squares for some models.*

2 *To apply the first layer, thin some PVA medium with a little water in an old container. Brush the solution onto the strips and lay them in the same direction across the mould, overlapping the strips. Use a knife or cocktail stick to press the strips into tight corners. Leave to dry. When not in use, cover the PVA solution with baking (aluminum) foil to prevent it from drying out.*

3 *Brush the PVA solution onto the previous layer before applying further layers. If you can use a different coloured paper for alternate layers, this will help differentiate between layers. Apply each layer at a different angle to the last to help strengthen the model. Strips can extend beyond the edges of a mould and can then be trimmed level with scissors or a craft knife when dry.*

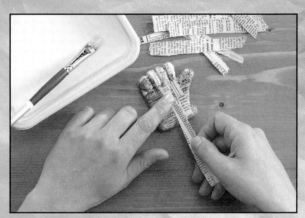

Papier mâché – pulp method

1 *Tear four double sheets of newspaper into pieces approximately 2.5 cm (1 in) square at the largest. Soak the pieces in water for at least 8 hours, then boil in a saucepan for 20 minutes to loosen the fibres. Tip the solution into a sieve and shake out the excess water.*

2 *Use a whisk or blender to blend the paper pieces to a pulp. Empty the pulp into a mixing bowl. Add three tablespoons of PVA medium, one tablespoon of linseed oil and three drips of oil of cloves to help prevent mould forming.*

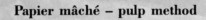

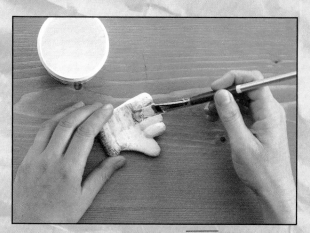

Sanding, filling and undercoating

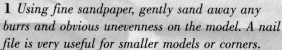

3 Mix together with a spoon, squashing the pulp into a solid lump. Now squeeze the pulp together in your hands. Keep the pulp in an airtight container in the fridge when not in use. As an alternative to making your own pulp, paper pulp available from art and craft stores or suppliers can be mixed with water to produce a versatile, hard-wearing papier mâché pulp.

1 Using fine sandpaper, gently sand away any burrs and obvious unevenness on the model. A nail file is very useful for smaller models or corners.

2 If you want a smooth, level finish to the design, prepare some wood filler according to the manufacturer's instructions. Smear the filler onto the model and set aside to harden. Sand again.

3 A layer of undercoat will prepare the surface for painting. Household undercoat or gesso, available from art stores or suppliers, can be used for this. Apply a second and third coat if the model is to be painted with Indian inks or if it is necessary to even out the surface a little more.

Salt dough

Salt dough is an ideal material with which to model a variety of hanging decorations and its ingredients are probably already at hand in your store cupboard. It can be made in advance and stored in an airtight bag in the fridge or freezer.

You will need: plain flour; salt; water; airtight plastic bags; watercolour paints; varnish.

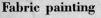

Fabric painting

1 Begin by washing, drying and pressing your fabric to remove any dressing or starch. Lay the prepared fabric over the design and secure together with masking tape. Transfer the design on to the fabric using a fine-point textile marker or a sharp HB pencil.

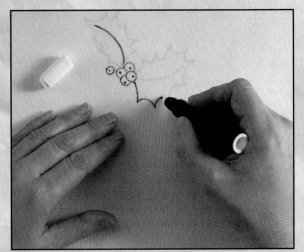

1 Mix 3 parts plain flour to 3 parts salt with about 1½ parts water, adding the water gradually. Knead into a flexible dough on a floured board if too sticky. Add a little cooking oil if necessary.

2 Roll out to a thickness of about 1 cm (⅜ in). Use pastry or biscuit cutters to cut shapes from the pastry. Cook the shapes in a medium to low-heated oven until they are biscuit hard.

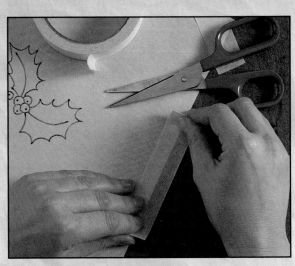

2 Position the transferred fabric over a large piece of card or layer of newspaper spread on a flat surface and secure firmly in place with strips of masking tape round the edge to prevent it from moving and smudging the wet paint.

3 *Always stir each pot of paint thoroughly before starting to work with it. Begin by filling in all the small areas of the design. Pour a little paint into a palette or saucer and apply to the fabric with an artist's small paintbrush.*

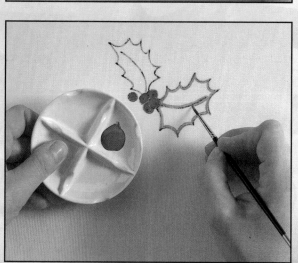

4 *Leave each colour to dry completely before applying the next. When changing colours, wash your brush and palette thoroughly in cold, clean water. Next, again using a small brush, carefully outline a group of large shapes with colour.*

5 *Fill in the outlined shapes with colour using a slightly larger brush, then move on to outline the next group of shapes. You may find it helpful to avoid smudging wet areas by remembering to work from left to right across the design if you are right-handed. For left-handed readers, work from right to left.*

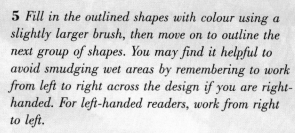

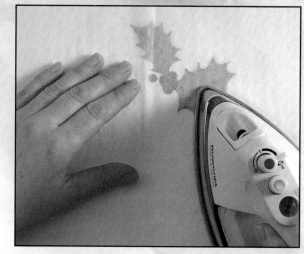

6 *When all painting is complete, allow to dry overnight. To fix the paint, lay a large sheet of white tissue paper or greaseproof paper over the painted areas and press with a hot iron following the manufacturer's instructions.*

15

Silk painting

1 Wash, dry and press the fabric to remove any dressing. Pin the fabric to a silk painting frame or wooden stretcher using three-point silk pins in preference to ordinary drawing pins or staples which will damage the fabric by making large holes in it. The fabric should be held taut across the frame.

2 Stir the chosen colour of outliner thoroughly and transfer it to the applicator bottle. Squeeze the applicator gently over a scrap piece of paper until the outliner flows evenly through the nozzle. Apply the outliner to the fabric.

3 Allow the outliner to dry completely. Shake or stir the silk paint vigorously. Apply the first colour using a cotton bud. Soak the bud in paint, then press it on to the fabric and allow the paint to flood across the outlined shape.

Square box

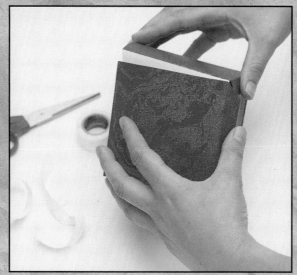

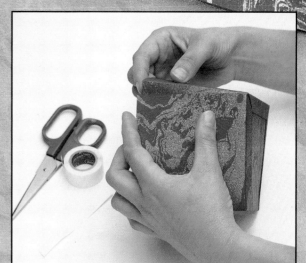

1 *Cut a square box from card (page 85). Score the back along broken lines and bend forward along scored lines. Apply double-sided tape to the tabs on the back of the base tabs and to the right side of the end tab. Stick the base tab under the base.*

2 *Stick the end tab under the opposite end.*

4 *Allow the first colour to dry for several hours, then apply the second colour using a fresh cotton bud. You will soon learn how much paint to apply, but remember that the heavier the coat of paint, the darker the finished result will be.*

5 *Allowing the paint to dry thoroughly between applications, add the remaining colours to the design in the same way as above, discarding and replacing the used cotton bud with a fresh one for each colour.*

6 *Leave to dry for 48 hours. To fix the colours, lay right side down over white tissue paper and press with a hot iron for two minutes. Rinse in cool water to remove surplus paint, allow to dry, then press lightly on the wrong side with a cool iron.*

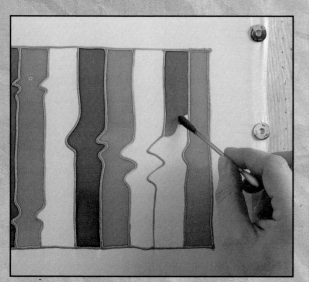

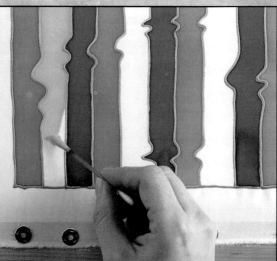

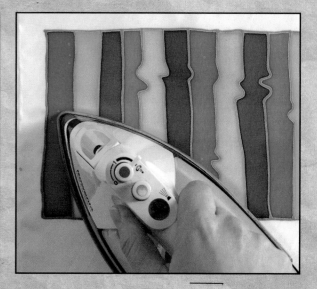

Paper decorations – double layer method

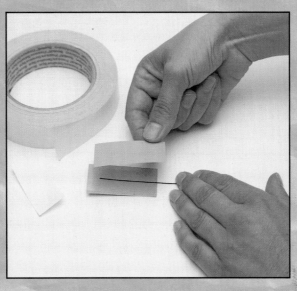

Single layer method

1 *Apply double-sided adhesive tape to paper, remove the backing tape and place a wire along the centre of the strip, extending downwards.*

2 *Starting at one edge, press a second layer of paper on top. Cut out the motif.*

Tape a length of wire to the back of the motif with the wire extending downwards from the shape.

Running Stitch

Running stitch is easy to work and looks good when the stitches are worked to an identical length. Also use as a strengthening stitch round cutwork designs. Work from right to left, picking up the fabric with an in-and-out movement.

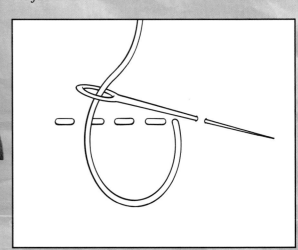

Back Stitch

Back stitch is very versatile - it makes a fine, delicate line of stitching which follows intricate designs well and it is also used to add linear details and outlines to cross stitched designs. When outlining cross stitch, it is often best to use a slightly finer thread for the back stitches – where the cross stitches are worked with three strands of stranded cotton, for example, use two strands for the accompanying back stitches. This prevents the cross stitched design being pulled out of shape.

Work back stitch from right to left, making small, even stitches which are worked forwards and backwards along the row. On plain fabric, keep the stitches small and regular so the line looks like machine stitching. On evenweave fabric, make each stitch cover the same number of fabric threads for woven blocks as each cross stitch.

Blanket Stitch

Blanket stitch is worked in the same way as buttonhole stitch (right), but here the stitches are spaced out evenly along the row. The stitch has a long history and the name comes from its traditional use as a finishing stitch for the edges of woven blankets. Today, it is used in appliqué and also as a decorative stitch in its own right.

Work blanket stitch from left to right, pulling the needle through the fabric over the top of the working thread to make a looped edge. Space the stitches evenly along the row or, to create a more decorative effect, change the length of the upright stitches to make them alternately long and short, or add a French knot (page 20) worked in a contrasting colour to the top of each upright.

Buttonhole Stitch

Buttonhole stitch, as well as being used as a decorative free embroidery stitch, makes a durable finish along a raw fabric edge. Although knotted variations such as tailor's buttonhole stitch are more hardwearing when working garment buttonholes, ordinary buttonhole stitch is perfect for cutwork, in which areas of the fabric are cut away to form an intricate design. The edges of the design are first strengthened with rows of running stitch (left) before the buttonhole stitches are worked. A flat, untwisted embroidery thread, such as stranded cotton, will give a closer finish than a rounded, twisted thread. Work from left to right, pulling the needle through the fabric over the top of the working thread. Position the stitches close together so that no fabric is visible.

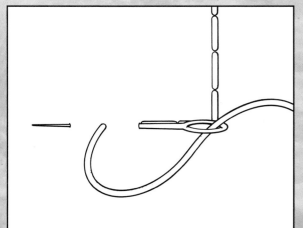

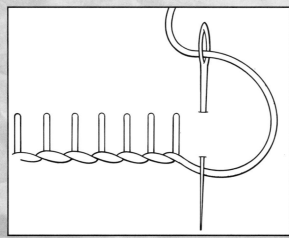

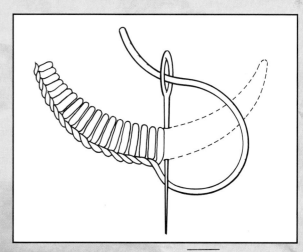

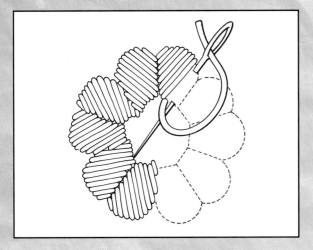

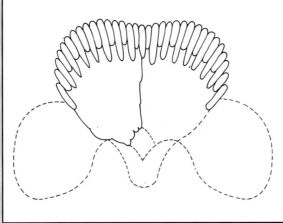

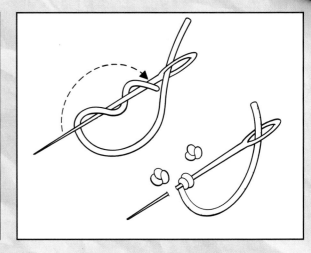

Satin Stitch

Work satin stitches in any direction as the changes of direction will create the effect of light and shade over the embroidered area. You can work the individual stitches of any length, but long stitches will tend to become loose and untidy, so you may need to split up large shapes into smaller, more manageable areas or work them in long and short stitch (right) for a similar, smoothly-stitched effect. Work satin stitch on fabric stretched in an embroidery hoop or frame to prevent puckering.

To work, carry the thread right across the shape to be filled and then return it underneath the fabric close to the point where the needle emerged. Position the stitches close together so they lie evenly and make a neat edge around the shape.

Long and Short Stitch

Long and short stitch is worked in a similar way to satin stitch (left), and gets its name from the long and short stitches used on the first row. A regular outline is created by the first row, then the inner rows produce an irregular line which allows colours to blend gradually into one another without a strongly defined line. Work long and short stitch in one colour to fill areas which are too large to be filled by ordinary satin stitch. Work the first row in alternately long and short satin stitches, following the contours of the shape and arranging the stitches closely together so that no fabric is visible. On the next journey, fit satin stitches of equal length into the spaces left on the first row. Continue until the shape is filled.

French Knot

French knots add splashes of colour and texture to a design. Use any type of embroidery thread, but remember that the weight of your thread will determine the size of the finished knot. French knots are quite tricky to work at first and you will need to practise them in order to work the knots neatly.

To work a French knot, bring the thread through the fabric and hold it taut with the left hand. Twist the needle round the thread two or three times and then tighten the twists. Still holding the thread in the left hand, turn the needle round and insert it in the fabric at the point where it originally emerged. Pull the needle and thread through the twists to the back of the fabric.

Cross Stitch

The top diagonal stitches in cross stitch designs should always slant from bottom left to top right. Work details and individual stitches by the method shown in the first two diagrams completing each cross before proceeding to the next. To cover large areas, work each row of stitches over two journeys. Work a row of diagonal stitches from right to left, as shown in the third diagram, then complete the crosses with a second row of stitches worked in the opposite direction.

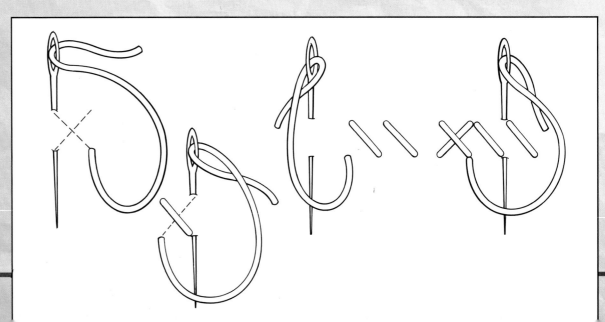

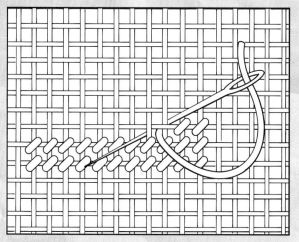

Tent Stitch

Tent stitch is a small, diagonal stitch which can be used for working designs from a chart (Needlepoint tree decorations, page 30) or for a design drawn directly on to the canvas (Floral pictures, page 62). The designs in this book are all worked on plastic canvas which eliminates tent stitch's ability to distort woven threads, so this stitch can be worked in horizontal rows, rather than by the more time-consuming diagonal method. Work in rows, taking a small stitch on the front of the canvas and a longer one on the reverse.

Double Leviathan Stitch

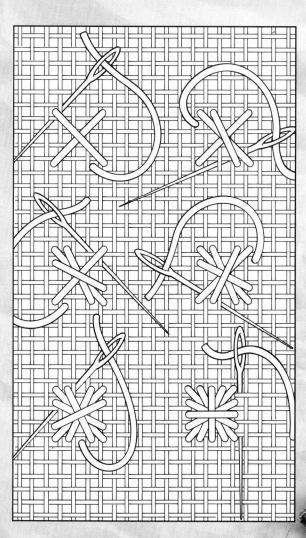

This stitch is used on canvas and produces a pattern of highly raised, square blocks made up of 8 overlapping stitches. The stitch is quite easy to work once you have practised the stitch sequence a few times. When working double leviathan stitch and tent stitch (above) together on the same piece, work the leviathan stitches first, then fill in round the edges with tent stitches. Begin by working a large individual cross stitch (left) over a square of 4 canvas threads. Then work a series of crossing stitches over the top of the original stitch, following the sequence shown, finishing with an upright cross stitch. Keep the tension of the overlapping stitches even and take care not to pull the thread tightly to avoid snapping the plastic canvas threads.

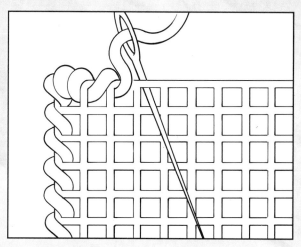

Overcast Stitch

Use to neaten single edges of plastic canvas and to join two pieces together. Plastic canvas does not fray, so do not allow turnings – align edges and stitch together. Work from left to right, taking one stitch through each hole, except at corners, where 3 stitches are made into the corner hole.

Hemming Stitch

Secure hems by hand in preference to machine for a neater look, although a machine-stitched hem will be more hardwearing. Turn up the hem and secure with pins or tacking stitches. Work from right to left, taking tiny stitches through both the fabric and the folded hem edge.

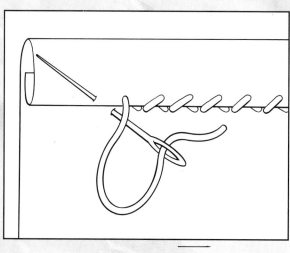

Decorations

Adorn your home at Christmas time with 'alternative' decorative trees, or ornament a traditional tree with luxurious hand-sewn and embroidered decorations; deck your mantelpiece, wall or door with sumptuous garlands and wreaths, and crown your festive table with stunning swags and centrepieces.

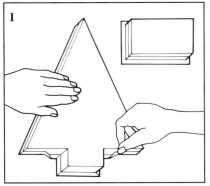

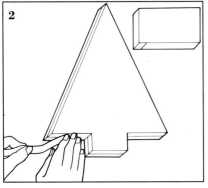

Following the diagram on page 88, cut 2 trees from 5 mm (¹/₄ in) thick foam board and 2 rectangles for the base 13 x 7 cm (5 x 2³/₄ in). Glue the tree pieces together, then the base pieces, using spray glue to make one tree. For the partridge and dove trees, apply green or gold paper to both sides of the trees and the bases with spray glue.

1 Cut off excess paper leaving a 6 mm (¹/₄ in) allowance. Wrap the allowance around the sides of the trees and the bases, snipping the corners to fit.

2 Apply double-sided adhesive tape to the back of a piece of the same paper you have used to cover the trees and cut strips 1 cm (³/₈ in) wide. Apply to the sides of the trees, joining the strips if necessary.

Three unusual and stylish Christmas trees. Make decorations of your own design to hang on the map pins. The bauble tree could be covered with purple metallic crêpe paper, as a vampish alternative, and teamed with silver baubles or other decorations of your choice.

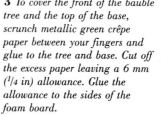

3 To cover the front of the bauble tree and the top of the base, scrunch metallic green crêpe paper between your fingers and glue to the tree and base. Cut off the excess paper leaving a 6 mm (¹/4 in) allowance. Glue the allowance to the sides of the foam board.

4 Cover the tree back and underside of the bauble tree base in the same way as the green and gold trees. Neaten the sides in the same way. Glue the trees centrally onto their bases.

5 Push map pins into the front side of the trees at intervals. Paint the pin heads to colour coordinate if you wish.

6 Cut a partridge and several pears from gold card or doves from white card using the templates on page 88. Attach a loop of gold thread to the back of each decoration. Hang the shapes on the map pins by the loops. Hang miniature glossy baubles on the bauble tree and add a star decoration to the top of the tree.

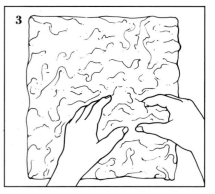

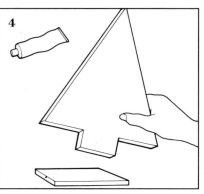

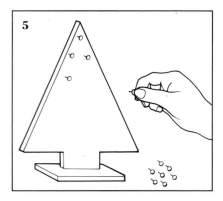

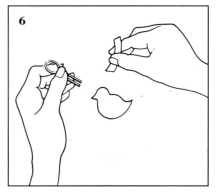

◄ As an unusual alternative to the traditional Christmas tree, why not make an elegant moss topiary which can be decorated with miniature baubles. Follow the instructions on the opposite page to make the topiary base, but use a foam cone in place of the rectangular pieces of foam. Trim the brown root part from clumps of bung moss. Squeeze glue from a glue gun onto the underside of the moss keeping your fingers well away from the hot glue. Place the moss clumps onto the cone as close together as possible. Glue baubles onto the moss to complete. You could make 2 matching trees to stand either side of a fireplace.

▶ A chunky topiary of plump, glossy artificial fruits which would make a colourful and original table centrepiece for a festive feast.

You will need:
A branch approximately
7.5 cm (3 in) in diameter,
20 cm (8 in) in length
Small artificial fruits such as
redcurrants, blackcurrants
and grapes
Large artificial fruits such as
apples and plums
Artificial leaves

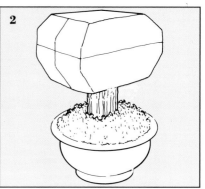

1 Fill a bowl three-quarters full with nylon-reinforced or quick-drying plaster. Set the branch in the centre of the bowl. When the plaster is dry, cover the top with moss.

2 Trim the ends of rectangular pieces of foam at an angle and glue together to form a large oblong with curved ends. Cut a 5 cm (2 in) deep hole in the base of the foam approximately the same diameter as the branch. Squeeze some glue from a glue gun into the hole and push the foam onto the branch. Trim stems of fruits to leave short lengths. Wire large fruits singly with 18 gauge wires; smaller fruits in small and large bunches (page 11). Cover all wires with stem binding tape (page 11). Position fruits close together in the foam. Intersperse artificial leaves.

Decorations

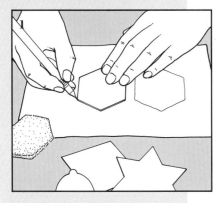

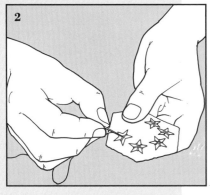

You will need:
Pieces of felt in yellow, orange,
pink, purple, green and blue
Selection of beads, sequins, bells
and earring shapes
DMC stranded cotton to match
the felt colours
Crewel needle size 8
Large needle with a long eye
Thin polyester wadding
Fine gold cord
Black felt pen with a fine point
Thin card
Craft knife
Pinking scissors

▶ *Indian-inspired beadwork and
brightly coloured felt shapes
combine to make a set of unusual
tree decorations which, with care,
will give pleasure for many years
to come.*

1 *Trace off the templates on
pages 80-81 and transfer to thin
card. Cut out the templates with
a craft knife. To make the front
pieces, place the templates on the
felt and draw round the outside
with a felt pen and cut out the
shapes. You will also need to cut
out corresponding back pieces
about 1.5 cm (¹/2 in) larger all
round from contrasting colours of
felt. Also cut out a piece of
wadding for each decoration,
slightly smaller than the
front piece.*

2 *Decorate the front pieces with
beads and sequins, using the
photographs as a guide to
spacing. To attach large sequins
with a central hole, use several
straight stitches radiating from
the hole or a single stitch plus a
small bead. Use two strands of
thread in the same colour as the
felt shape when attaching both
beads and sequins.*

3 *To assemble, place a front piece right side up over the corresponding back piece. Slip a piece of wadding between the two and secure with a few pins. Blanket stitch (page 19) round the edge with two strands of matching thread.*

4 *Cut away the surplus felt on the back piece with pinking scissors to make a decorative edge. Stitch a bell or earring shape to the bottom of the decoration, then thread a short length of gold cord through the large needle and insert it through the top to make a hanging loop.*

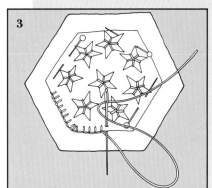

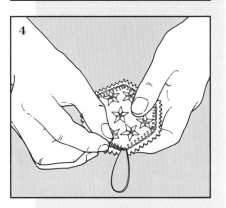

29

Decorations

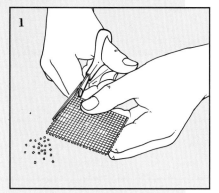

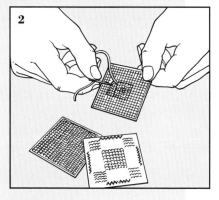

1 Cut out the squares of canvas, making sure that each one is exactly the same size, 20 threads square. Carefully trim off any tiny bumps of plastic round each piece so that the outer edge is perfectly smooth.

2 Following the charts on page 81, make 12 front pieces by working each design twice, using tent stitch (page 21) and double leviathan stitch (page 21) and leaving one complete thread unworked round each piece. Work 12 plain back pieces in tent stitch, 4 in each thread colour, again leaving the unworked thread.

You will need:
(to make 12 decorations)
24 5 cm (2 in) squares of 10
mesh plastic canvas (each piece
should be 24 threads square)
1 large hank each of DMC
tapestry wool in white; bright red
7606; green 7344
Tapestry needle size 22
Selection of white, green, red
and gold yarns to make tassels
Piece of thick card
12 cm (5 in) wide
12 gold coloured jump rings
7.20 m (8 yd) narrow
gold ribbon

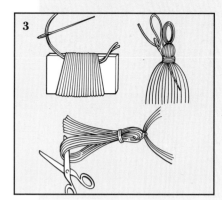

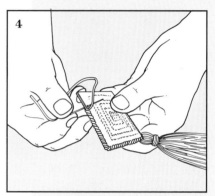

◀ *Squares of plastic canvas
stitched with geometric designs in
green, red and white are finished
with thick, luxurious tassels and
gold ribbon bows to create a set
of elegant tree decorations.*

3 *Gather a group of yarns
together and wrap several times
round the card. Cut a 30 cm
(12 in) length of matching yarn
and thread it through the strands
at one end of the card. Holding
both ends of the yarn, remove the
card and tie the ends of yarn
securely. Wrap a second length
of yarn tightly and evenly round
the strands 1.5 cm (¹/₂ in) from
the top and secure the end by
inserting it down through the
tassel. Cut the loops at the
bottom. Make four tassels in
each colour.*

4 *Stitch a tassel securely to one
corner of the front piece on the
wrong side. Place the front and
back piece together with wrong
sides facing. Using a contrasting
colour of tapestry wool, overcast
the two pieces together, catching
in a jump ring at the corner
opposite the tassel. Finish off the
thread end securely. Repeat for the
remaining pieces. Thread 60 cm
(24 in) of gold ribbon through
the jump rings.*

31

Decorations

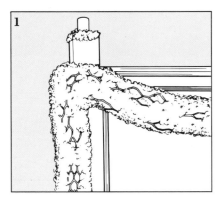

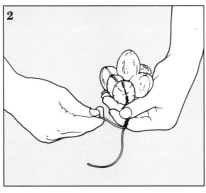

You will need:
Wire netting
Terracotta pots
Bunches of gold grapes
Large cinnamon sticks
Walnuts
Dried red roses
Fir cones, some sprayed gold
Woodland cones
Artificial plums
Lychin and sphagnum moss
Velvet or an alternative
furnishing fabric
Wire-edged ribbon

▶ *Complete this dramatic fireplace display by tying decorative wire-edged ribbon around the cinnamon bundles so that it conceals the wire, and add a large double-looped bow to the centre point of the swag (page 10).*

1 *Make a swag base (page 10) long enough to loop across mantelpiece with a length hanging down either side. Secure in place with nails or by threading wire through back of mantelpiece. Twist fabric loosely around swag beginning in centre and working outwards. Wire in place at ends of swag. Fill pots with foam and wire (page 11). Push wires through swag to netting on far side and twist onto wire.*

2 *Mount nuts onto wire stems (page 11) and wire together in large bunches. Fill pots with walnuts and roses. Wire fruits in groups of 3-4, bunches of grapes singly, cinnamon sticks in bunches and cones (page 11). Wire onto swag, interspersed with clumps of lychin moss.*

Decorations

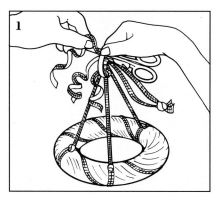

1 *Bind a willow ring with tartan giftwrapping ribbon, applying glue to the ends and pushing them into the willow. Cut 6 1-m (40-in) lengths of tartan ribbon. Tie the free ends of the lengths of ribbon around the ring, dividing it into thirds, extending ribbons 25 cm (10 in) above the knot. Pull the free ends smoothly over the back of a pair of scissors to curl them.*

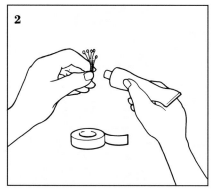

2 *Bunch together about 12 yellow stamen strings and bend in half. Dab with glue close to the fold. When the glue has dried, bind together with floral tape.*

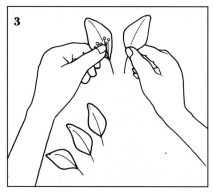

3 *To make a poinsettia flower, use the clematis template on page 88 to cut 6 petals from red paper and to make 2 leaves from green paper following the double layer method on page 18. Bind 3 petals to the stamens with floral tape, then add the remaining 3 between them. Make about 6 or 7 poinsettias and 12-14 leaves.*

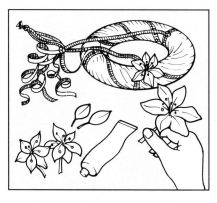

4 *Bind the wire stems of the leaves with floral tape. Dab glue onto the poinsettia wires and push into the ring. Dab leaf stems in the same way and position 2 leaves each side of every flower.*

▲ When hung on a door, this sparkling wreath would signal a suitably festive welcome to party guests.

◀ Surface space is often in short supply during the festive season; therefore suspending a decorated ring from the ceiling exploits a further spacial dimension.

1 Cut metallic crêpe paper 150 x 24 cm (60 x 10 in) and join the short ends together on the reverse of the paper with adhesive tape.

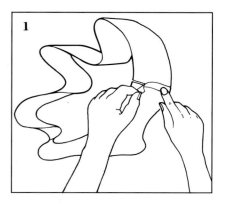

2 Place a 25 cm (10 in) diameter dry foam ring in the middle of the circle of paper. Staple the long edges of the paper together to enclose the ring, arranging the join under the ring.

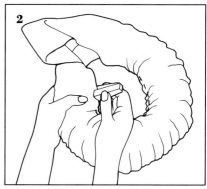

3 Wrap 4 small boxes with foil giftwrap and fasten with giftwrapping ribbon. Bend lengths of wire in half and thread through the ribbon on the underside of the boxes. Thread wire through the rings of glossy baubles in the same way.

4 Arrange the boxes and larger baubles on opposite sides of the ring, pushing the wires into the ring. Make some stars from metallic card using the templates on page 88 and following the single layer method on page 18. Push the wire 'stems' into the ring together with some smaller baubles. Drape a string of beads around the ring, gluing the ends on the underside.

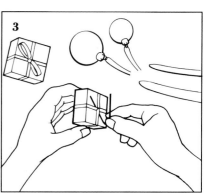

Decorations

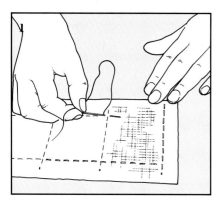

1 *Using tacking stitches, mark out 6 identical divisions measuring 25 fabric blocks square on each green fabric strip. Mark the centre of each square with a couple of tacking stitches.*

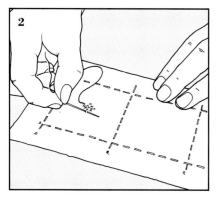

2 *Using the photograph as a guide, work a snowflake motif from the chart (page 81) in cross stitch (page 20) at the centre of each square. Then work the corresponding numbers (page 81) in back stitch (page 19), placing the numbers 2 squares inside the tacked lines. Use 3 strands of thread in the tapestry needle throughout.*

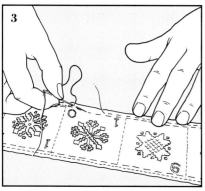

3 *Trim away surplus fabric allowing a margin of 8 blocks outside the tacked lines. Turn under 6 blocks all round, leaving a 2 block margin showing on the right side, and tack in place. Using the gold thread, work back stitch along the lines indicated by the original tacking, removing the tacking stitches as you go. Press lightly on the wrong side.*

4 *Arrange the strips in the correct sequence on the white fabric, leaving a gap of 8 blocks between the strips. Pin the strips in position. Using the transparent thread, machine stitch along the sides and lower edge of each strip, forming pockets by taking the stitching up to the top edge and back down again when you reach the vertical gold lines dividing the snowflakes.*

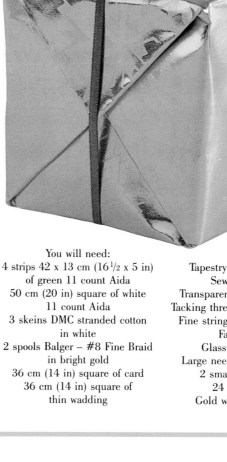

You will need:
4 strips 42 x 13 cm (16$\frac{1}{2}$ x 5 in)
of green 11 count Aida
50 cm (20 in) square of white
11 count Aida
3 skeins DMC stranded cotton
in white
2 spools Balger – #8 Fine Braid
in bright gold
36 cm (14 in) square of card
36 cm (14 in) square of
thin wadding

Tapestry needle size 24
Sewing needle
Transparent machine thread
Tacking thread in a light colour
Fine string or crochet cotton
Fabric glue
Glass-headed pins
Large needle with long eye
2 small brass rings
24 small gifts
Gold wrapping paper

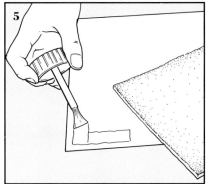

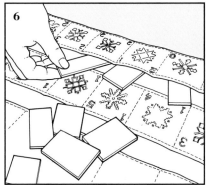

5 *Spread fabric glue over one side of the card. Lay the wadding over the card, matching the sides, and gently press in place. Allow the glue to dry thoroughly. Following the instructions on pages 52-53, lace the white fabric over the padded card with string or crochet cotton. Leave a margin of 3 fabric blocks showing round the sides and along the lower edge and 2 blocks along the top edge.*

6 *Stitch a brass ring securely to the top corners on the back of the calendar. Wrap the gifts neatly with gold paper and tuck a gift into each pocket. Tap two picture pins into the wall to correspond with the rings and hang up the calendar, or stand the calendar on a shelf or piece of furniture.*

◀ *Wrap 24 presents and open one on each day of December until the big day finally arrives! Tiny notebooks, chocolate bars, puzzles and packs of small coloured pencils make good gifts.*

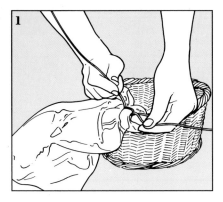

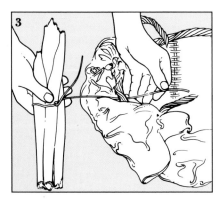

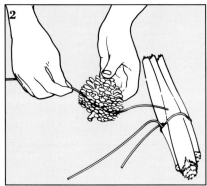

1 *Attach fabric to basket rim at 15 cm (6 in) intervals with 22 gauge wires (page 11).*

2 *Mount cones onto 18 gauge wires (page 11). Spray with gold paint. Wire bunches of cinnamon sticks together (page 11).*

3 *Attach cinnamon bundles and cones to basket rim with wire 'stems'. Trim excess wires. Tie ribbon around each cinnamon bundle to cover wire.*

▼ *If you wish to fill the basket with pot pourri, line the basket with fabric before you begin.*

You will need:
A basket
Gold paint
Large cinnamon sticks
Cones
Fabric
Ribbon

You will need:·
A 30 cm (12 in) diameter
foam ring
Bunches of gold grapes
Lavender
Marjoram
Woodland cones
Small dried red roses

Artificial plums
4 candles and candleholders
Wire-edged ribbon
Wire lavender and marjoram in very small bunches with 22 gauge wires and wire woodland cones (page 11). Cover all stems with stem binding tape (page 11).

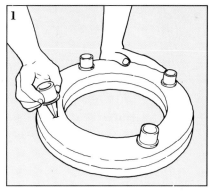

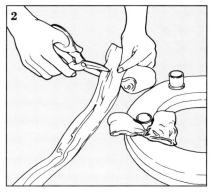

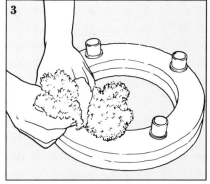

1 Position candleholders at equal distances around ring, pushing bases into foam.

2 Cut ribbon into 8 equal lengths and make single loop bows without tails (page 10). Place 2 bows by each candleholder.

3 Mount candles, then position cones. Add lavender, then marjoram and roses. Complete with artificial plums and gold grapes.

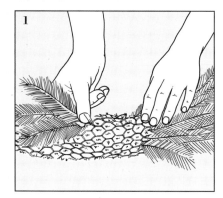

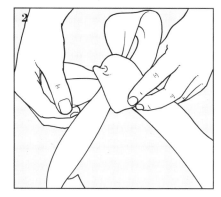

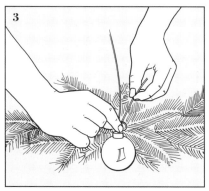

1 *Make a swag base following the instructions on page 10. Cover with evergreen foliage, tucking stems in firmly and working from the centre outwards.*

2 *Make 2 bows from wire-edged ribbon. Wire onto swag.*

3 *Wire baubles at equal intervals along swag.*

1 *Make salt dough following the instructions on page 14. Roll out to about 75 mm (¹/₄ in) thick. Cut out Christmas shapes with pastry or biscuit cutters. Pierce a hole at the top of each shape for hanging and at the bottom of bell shapes to add a 'clapper'. Bake the shapes. Paint the pieces, then varnish 5 times to give a high gloss finish.*

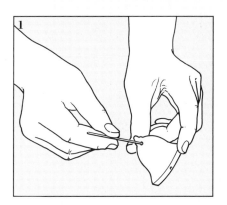

2 *Paint details on the bell shapes with gold paint. Hang shapes on glitter thread, tying the knot just above the hole so that they hang straight. Glue gold bows to the tops of the bells.*

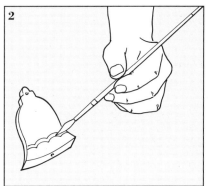

◀ ▲ *Bring a festive air to the buffet table by using Christmas baubles and bows to create a decorative evergreen swag. Alternatively, adorn a fir-clad swag base with glittering salt dough decorations which are so quick and easy to make.*

3 *Push a pipecleaner into a bead. Cut the end about 1 cm (³/₈ in) above the bead. Glue the end into the hole at the bottom of the bell.*

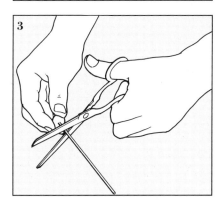

▲ *These painted salt dough decorations in gold, silver and scarlet look equally effective hanging from a simple arrangement of twigs in a jug as on a grand evergreen swag.*

Decorations

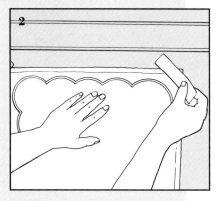

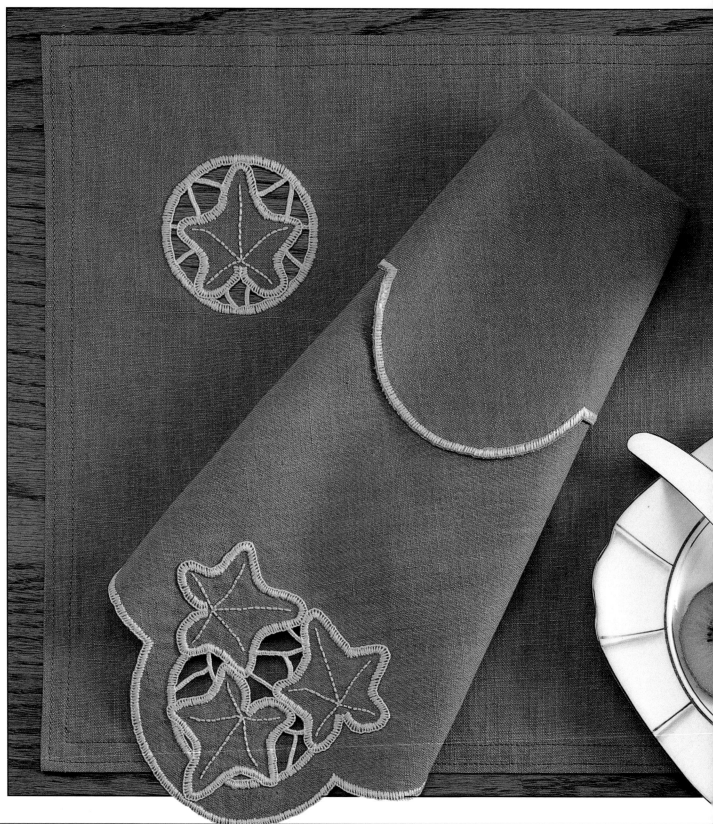

1 *Trace off the napkin motif and scalloped border on page 83 on to paper with the felt pen, repeating the scallop shapes several times as shown to make a border.*

2 *Tape the tracing to a window and secure the square of fabric centrally over the top with strips of masking tape. You should be able to see the traced design through the fabric quite clearly on a bright day - alternatively, use a sheet of glass propped between two dining chairs and direct light upwards from an adjustable table lamp. Draw the design lines on the fabric using the embroidery marker.*

You will need:
45 cm (17³/4 in) square of green
linen for each napkin
plus 46 x 33 cm (18 x 13 in) for
each tablemat
DMC stranded cotton in white
(you will need 3 skeins to stitch
one napkin and one tablemat)
Crewel needle size 7
Green sewing cotton
Black felt pen with a fine point
Water-soluble embroidery marker
Masking tape

◀ *Stylish yet casual in apple green and white, this design can also be worked in white thread on white linen napkins to grace a formal dinner table.*

3 *Three strands of thread are used for all the embroidery. Begin by working the plain bars which join two edges of the ivy motifs together - work running stitch (page 18) round the motif until the position for a bar is reached. Strand the thread back and forth 3 times between the motifs, then cover the threads with buttonhole stitch (page 19) and continue the running stitch until the next bar is reached.*

4 *Work branched bars in the same way to join 3 edges of the ivy motifs together, but add a third 'leg' to the stranded threads as shown. Continue working running stitch around the motif. Next, work buttonhole stitch round the ivy shapes, making sure that the looped edge faces outwards. Embroider the leaf veins in back stitch.*

5 *Work 2 rows of running stitch round the scalloped edge, then work buttonhole stitch over the outlines making sure that the looped edge faces outwards. Using small, sharp scissors, cut away the portions of fabric behind the bars. Cut slowly and carefully and take care not to snip into any stitches. Finally, cut away the fabric round the scalloped edge, then rinse in cold water to remove the embroidery marker. Press on the wrong side with a hot iron.*

6 *Transfer the tablemat motif on page 83 to one corner of the fabric reetangle and work the cutwork motif in the same way, making sure that the looped edge of the buttonhole stitches outlines the portions of the fabric to be cut away. Turn and pin a narrow hem round the mat and finish off with 2 rows of machine stitching using matching thread, or hem by hand (page 21). Rinse and press as above.*

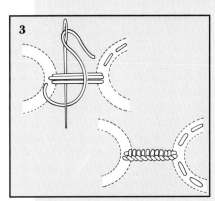

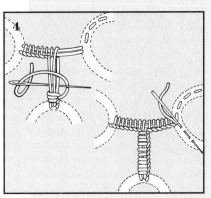

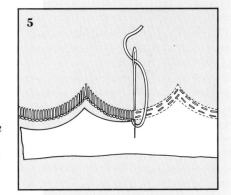

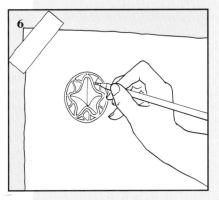

Decorations

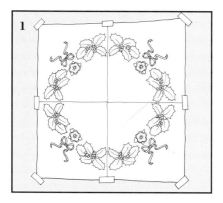

1 *Trace off the design on page 82 4 times using the fine-point felt pen. Stick the 4 tracings together, as shown, to make a large circular design. Secure to a flat surface with strips of masking tape.*

You will need:
Large piece of thin, closely-woven cream cotton fabric, at least 120 cm (48 in) square
Black textile marker with a fine point
Fabric paint in metallic gold, pearly opaque white, grey green

Glass-headed pins
Strips of thick card
Artist's paintbrushes
Black felt pen with permanent ink
Masking tape
Cream sewing thread

▶ *Surround a Christmas centrepiece complete with festive candle with a cream fabric tablecentre decorated with a hand-painted design in soft green, pearly white and gold.*

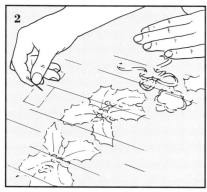

2 *Press the fabric well. Lay it centrally over the traced design and secure with strips of masking tape. To prevent movement round the edges of the design, push fine glass-headed pins through the fabric into the strips of masking tape holding down the tracings.*

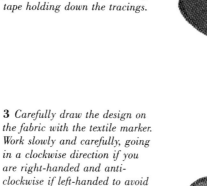

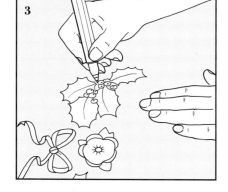

3 *Carefully draw the design on the fabric with the textile marker. Work slowly and carefully, going in a clockwise direction if you are right-handed and anti-clockwise if left-handed to avoid smudging the lines. Allow to dry.*

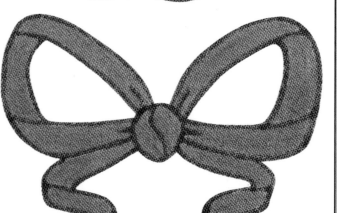

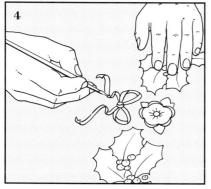

4 *Paint (pages 14-15) the design on the stretched fabric without removing the tracing. Stir the pot of gold fabric paint with a narrow strip of thick card. Using a small brush, fill in the bows, holly berries, flower centres and petal edges with gold paint, working in the same direction as above. Allow to dry – this may take several hours, depending on the temperature of the room.*

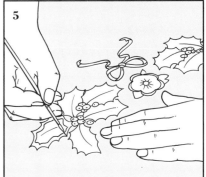

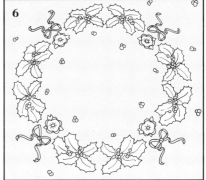

5 *Stirring each pot of paint before application, carefully fill in the flowers with white paint and the leaves with grey green, taking care not to paint over the flower stamens and leaf veins. Make sure you let each colour dry thoroughly before proceeding to the next.*

6 *Finally, use the textile marker to dot tiny groups of holly berries at random over the plain areas of fabric. Fill in the berries with gold paint as above. Fix the painted areas as shown on page 15. Turn a narrow hem round the cloth and secure with a row of machine stitching or hand hemming (page 21) using matching thread.*